Magical Unicorn Academy

Adding and Subtracting

ARCTURUS

Key skills in this book

ARCTURUS

This edition published in 2022 by Arcturus Publishing Limited
26/27 Bickels Yard, 151–153 Bermondsey Street,
London SE1 3HA

Copyright © Arcturus Holdings Limited

Author: Lisa Regan
Illustrator: Sam Loman
Editors: Becca Clunes and Donna Gregory
Designer: Linda Storey
Managing Editor: Joe Harris

ISBN: 978-1-3988-0398-5
CH008631NT
Supplier 29, Date 1121, Print run 11797

Printed in China

Introduction

Welcome to Magical Unicorn Academy! These unicorns and all their friends in the enchanted forest are excited to learn all about the magic of mathematics—and they need your help!

This book is packed with fun activities to teach you addition and subtraction. Start at the beginning, where you'll learn the skills you need to start adding and subtracting small numbers. Then, when you feel confident, start working through the book. The activities will get harder, but don't worry—you'll be getting better and better as you go. Soon, you'll be adding and subtracting big numbers easily!

One to Ten

Make Starbright happy by writing the numbers 1 to 10.

1	_____	one	_____
2	_____	two	_____
3	_____	three	_____
4	_____	four	_____
5	_____	five	_____
6	_____	six	_____
7	_____	seven	_____
8	_____	eight	_____
9	_____	nine	_____
10	_____	ten	_____

Counting Fun

Springblossom loves to dress up! Count how many of each kind of item he has.

Dot to Dot

What is Sparkle building in her workshop?
Join the dots from 1 to 20 to find out.

Under the Sea

Can you find Masie's undersea friend?
Start at 20 and join the dots, counting back until you get to 1.

Caterpillar Counting

Fill in the missing numbers on the caterpillars' bodies.

First caterpillar: 1, 2, 3, 4, 5, 6, 7, 8, 9, 10

Second caterpillar: 2, 3, 4, 5, 6, 7, 8, 9, 10, 11

Third caterpillar: 4, 5, 6, 7, 8, 9, 10, 11, 12, 13

Hide and Seek

Fill in the numbers that are missing under these rainbows.
Can you see the unicorn friends hiding in some of them?

10   11   12   13   14

6

15   16   17   18   19

6

6

20   21   22   23   24

More, Please!

Fill in the missing numbers on these cupcakes. Add one each time, like the first example.

 **2**    **3**    **4**

 **4**

 **7**

 **9**

10

Less and More

Fill in the blanks by writing numbers that are
one less and one more than the numbers in the middle.

one less (subtract 1)		one more (add 1)
	5	
	8	
	4	
	6	
	2	
	7	
	10	
	9	
	3	

Fairy Friends

How many flowers does each fairy have?
Count them and add one more.

 + 🌼 = 3

 + 🌸 =

🌼🌼🌼🌼🌼 + 🌼 =

🌼🌼🌼 + 🌼 =

A Fairy Feast

The fairies are putting on a spread for their unicorn friends! Count the foods, and add one more to each group.

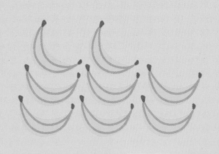

$$3 + 1 = 4 \qquad \boxed{} + \boxed{} = \boxed{}$$

$$\boxed{} + \boxed{} = \boxed{} \qquad \boxed{} + \boxed{} = \boxed{}$$

$$\boxed{} + \boxed{} = \boxed{}$$

13

Mathemagical

The fairies love casting spells! Take away one star from each spell. How many are left each time? The first one has been done for you.

★ ★ − ★ = **1**

★ ★ ★ − ★ =

★ ★ ★ ★ ★ − ★ =

★ ★ ★ ★ − ★ =

★ ★ ★ ★ ★ ★ − ★ =

14

Fly and Be Free

One butterfly from each group flies away.
Subtract 1 to find out how many are left.

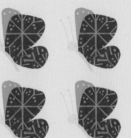

$$\boxed{3} - \boxed{1} = \boxed{2} \qquad \boxed{} - \boxed{} = \boxed{}$$

$$\boxed{} - \boxed{} = \boxed{} \qquad \boxed{} - \boxed{} = \boxed{}$$

$$\boxed{} - \boxed{} = \boxed{}$$

At the Beach

The unicorns love to visit their merfriends at the beach. Use the number lines to help the mermaids do these addition problems.

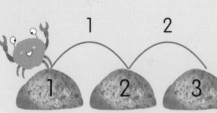

If Crab crawls over two rocks, what number rock does he get to?

$$1 + 2 =$$

What number rock does he get to if he climbs over two more?

$$3 + 2 =$$

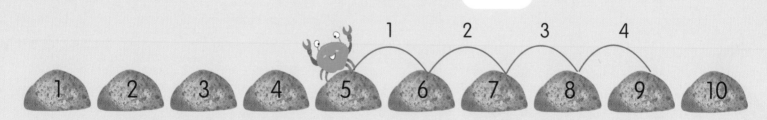

What number rock does he get to if he climbs over four more?

$$5 + 4 =$$

Clever Foals

Help Bambino and Booboo solve these problems using the number line.

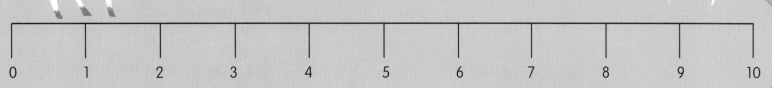

0 1 2 3 4 5 6 7 8 9 10

2 + 5 =

5 + 2 =

7 + 3 =

6 + 1 =

4 + 2 =

1 + 9 =

7 + 1 =

6 + 3 =

3 + 2 =

4 + 3 =

Giving Away Jewels

Can you find the answers to these subtraction problems?
Use the lines of jewels to help you count backward.

2   1

 1 2 3 4 5 6 7 8 9 10

Elfie has ten jewels. She gives two to her sister, Ivy. How many does Elfie have now?

10 – 2 =

3   2   1

 1 2 3 4 5 6 7 8 9 10

She gives three to her friend Fern. How many jewels are left?

8 – 3 =

4   3   2   1

 1 2 3 4 5 6 7 8 9 10

Elfie gives four jewels to Jack. Now how many jewels does Elfie have?

5 – 4 =

Lilac's Number Line

Help Lilac find the answers to these problems.
Use the number line to help you.

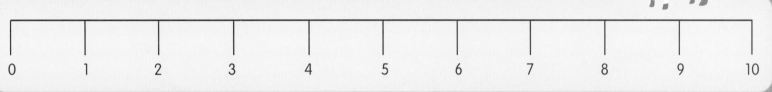

0   1   2   3   4   5   6   7   8   9   10

10 – 3 =

8 – 6 =

5 – 1 =

9 – 4 =

10 – 2 =

7 – 3 =

6 – 1 =

3 – 2 =

10 – 8 =

9 – 5 =

A Hive of Activity

Each of Jasper's beehives is home to ten bees. Draw in the missing bees and write how many you have added.

2 +

5 +

7 +

4 +

1 +

Adding to Ten

Pairs of numbers that add up to ten are called number bonds. Help Missy and Miranda think of five different number bonds.

[ ] + [ ] = 10

[ ] + [ ] = 10

[ ] + [ ] = 10

[ ] + [ ] = 10

[ ] + [ ] = 10

It doesn't matter which way round you put the numbers: 9 + 1 is the same as 1 + 9.

Blown Away

Fionne has found a flower with ten petals.
How many petals are left if …

1 blows
away?

2 blow
away?

3 blow
away?

4 blow
away?

5 blow
away?

6 blow
away?

7 blow
away?

8 blow
away?

9 blow
away?

10 blow
away?

Remember, Remember

Missy and Miranda are trying to remember the number bonds
to help with their subtraction puzzles. Can you help?

10 − ☐ = ☐

10 − ☐ = ☐

10 − ☐ = ☐

10 − ☐ = ☐

10 − ☐ = ☐

From the Trees

Help Fairy Floss count the falling leaves or fruits in each group.
Then add together the groups in each problem.

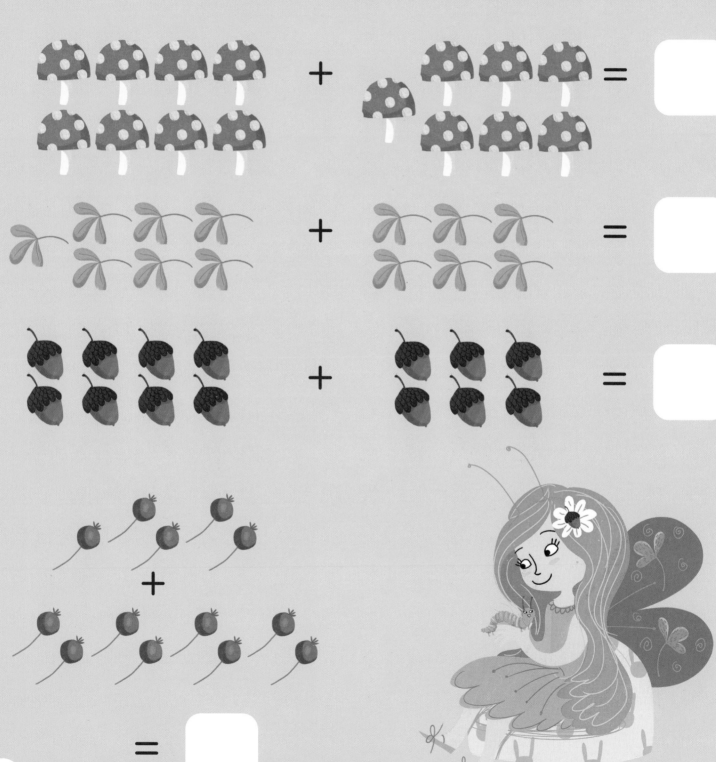

Say It With Flowers

How many flowers are in each group? Count them and fill in the numbers in the boxes before adding them up.

 +  +

□ + □ = □

□ + □ = □

□ + □ = □

□ + □ = □

□ + □ = □

From Zero to Hero

Zero is another word for nothing or none. Do you know what happens when you add or subtract zero? Find out with Maia and Myrtle!

Mya sees two octopuses.
None of them swims off to hide. How many are left?

2 - 0 =

There are four crabs on the ocean floor. No other crabs join them.
How many are there?

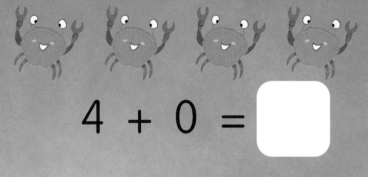

4 + 0 =

Milly collects seven pink shells. She doesn't give any away.
How many does she take home?

7 - 0 =

Adding On

Fairies Flora and Fatima have such fun making daisy chains. They add more to make them longer and longer! Can you work out the adding problems?

3 + 1 = ⬜

4 + 2 = ⬜

6 + 1 = ⬜

2 + 3 = ⬜

5 + 5 = ⬜

4 + 0 = ⬜

1 + 3 = ⬜

2 + 4 = ⬜

1 + 6 = ⬜

3 + 2 = ⬜

2 + 2 = ⬜

0 + 4 = ⬜

Paint a Rainbow

Solve the adding problems in the key so that
you can finish this beautiful picture.

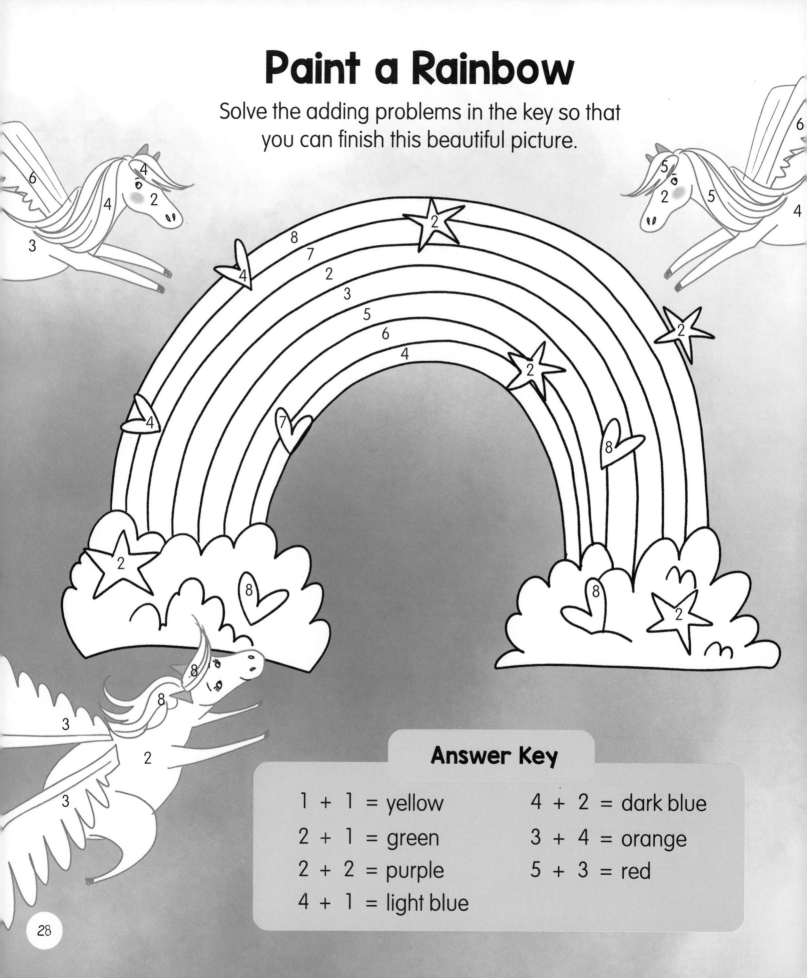

Answer Key

1 + 1 = yellow   4 + 2 = dark blue

2 + 1 = green   3 + 4 = orange

2 + 2 = purple   5 + 3 = red

4 + 1 = light blue

In the Pink

Help Rosebud fill in the pink fluffy clouds
with the answers to the adding problems.

$4 + 5 =$

$3 +$ $= 3$

$2 +$ $= 10$

$+ 5 = 10$

$+ 3 = 8$

$2 + 2 =$

$5 + 2 =$

$2 +$ $= 8$

$3 +$ $= 9$

$+ 2 = 6$

$6 + 1 =$

Sharing Is Caring

Moonbeam is giving some of his party treats to the others. How many does he have left?

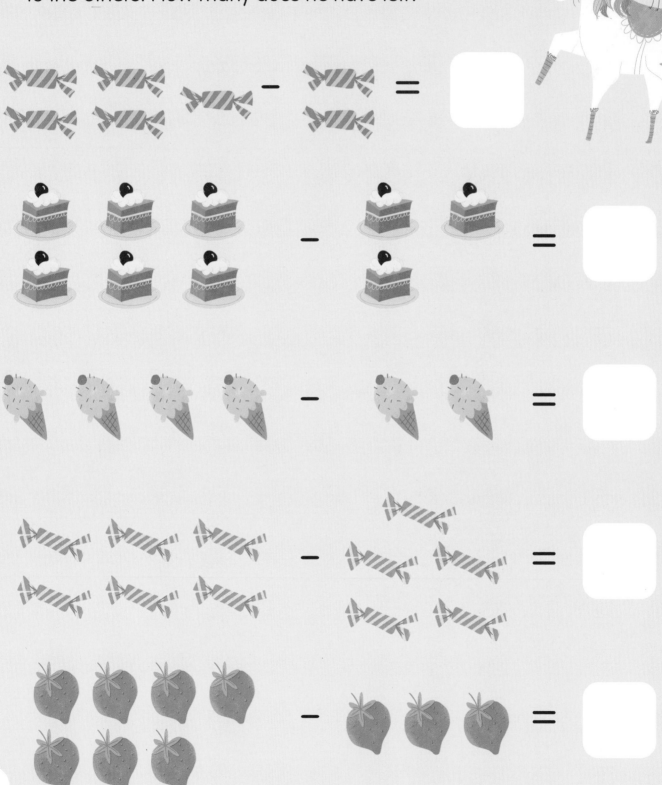

Happy Hair Day

Marigold keeps losing her hair accessories.
Work out how many she has left each time.

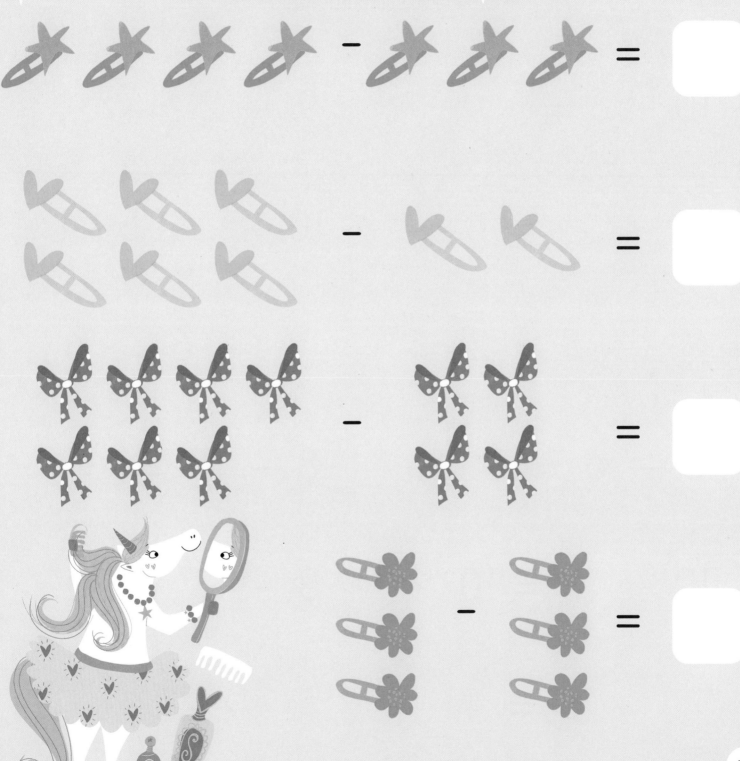

Take It Away!

Twinkle and Aisha are struggling with these problems. Can you help them fill in the missing numbers?

$10 - 5 = \boxed{}$

$9 - 2 = \boxed{}$

$6 - \boxed{} = 4$

$10 - \boxed{} = 4$

$\boxed{} - 5 = 2$

$\boxed{} - 6 = 6$

$8 - 6 = \boxed{}$

$8 - 1 = \boxed{}$

$10 - \boxed{} = 10$

$3 - \boxed{} = 2$

$\boxed{} - 0 = 4$

$\boxed{} - 2 = 7$

Under the Sea

Complete the picture by solving each problem
and use the key to see which shades to use.

Answer Key

5 − 2 = pink

3 + 5 = red

4 + 3 = turquoise

2 + 2 = yellow

7 − 1 = green

10 − 5 = blue

Caterpillar Calculations

Does the caterpillar need to add or subtract items to make these problems right? Fill in the missing signs to help.

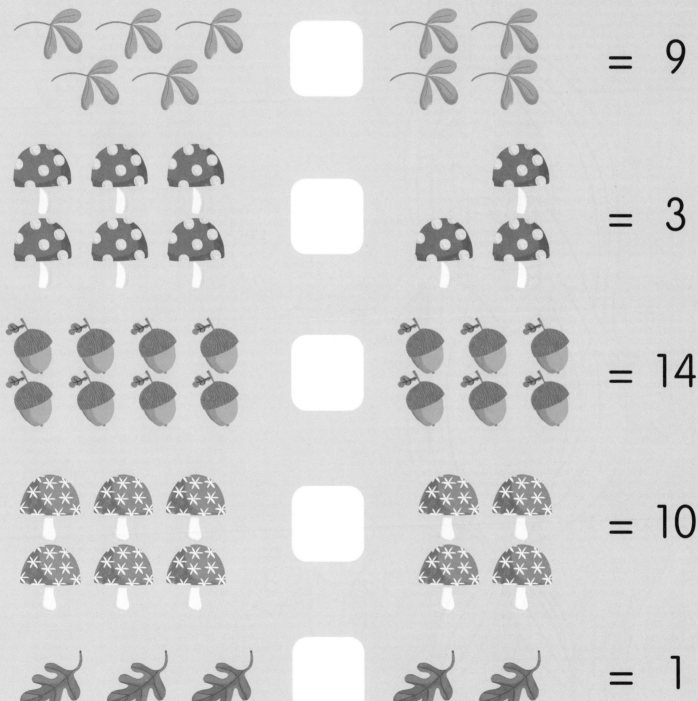

= 9

= 3

= 14

= 10

= 1

Rainy Days

Each of these umbrellas should have ten flowers on it. Work out whether flowers need to be added, or taken away.

$$12 \; \bigcirc \; \boxed{} = 10$$

$$6 \; \bigcirc \; \boxed{} = 10$$

$$5 \; \bigcirc \; \boxed{} = 10$$

$$3 \; \bigcirc \; \boxed{} = 10$$

Doubling Dots

Count the dots on the front of each sea creature,
and draw the same number at the back.
How many dots does each have?

$3 + 3 =$

$5 + 5 =$

$2 + 2 =$

$6 + 6 =$

$4 + 4 =$

Fishy Fun

If half of the fish in each group swim away from Marissa, how many are left? Cross out half the total if you need to, and write the answer.

$$2 - 1 =$$

$$8 - 4 =$$

$$10 - 5 =$$

$$4 - 2 =$$

$$6 - 3 =$$

More Wishes

If the second magic frog grants the same number of
wishes as the first, how many wishes are there in total on each line?

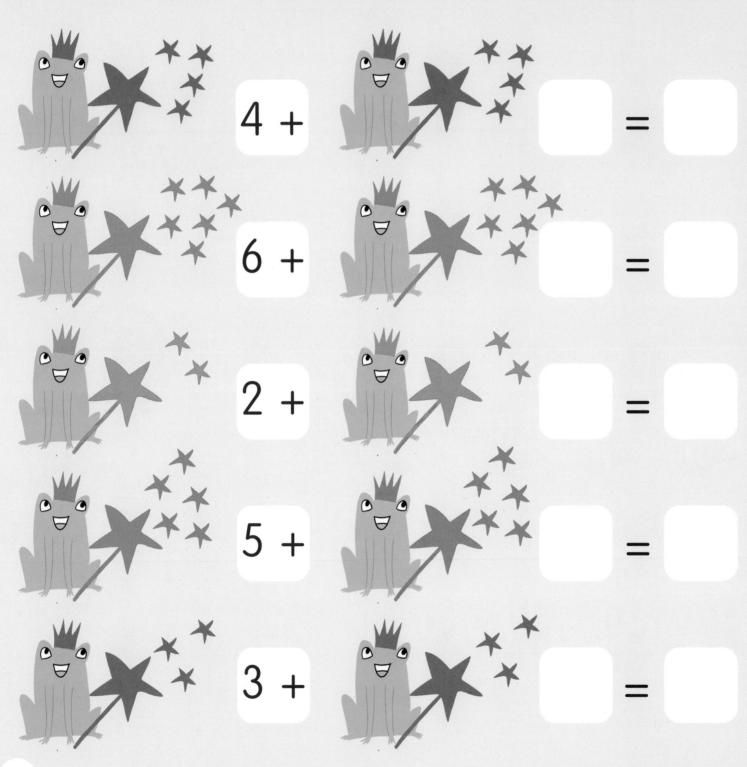

4 +   =

6 +   =

2 +   =

5 +   =

3 +   =

Pick Me!

Flossie is collecting flowers for her friends. If she picks half from each flower patch, how many will be left?

A Perfect Match

Match each unicorn with its chosen treat by solving the calculations.

8 – 3

11

5 – 2

6

8 + 3

7

9 – 3

10 – 3

3

5

Twin Twos

Which of these calculations has 2 as the answer?
Help the rainbow twins work it out.

$10 + 0 = $ 10

$11 - 6 = $ 16

$6 - 1 = $ 7

$5 + 2 = $ 7

$7 + 3 = $ 10

$8 - 6 = $ 14

$6 + 1 = $ 7

$4 + 2 = $ 6

$2 + 3 = $ 7

$7 - 4 = $ 12

$6 - 0 = $ 6

$12 - 10 = $ 22

Money Match

How many coins need to go in each purple coin purse to make it the same amount as the lefthand purse each time?

42

Shell Sharing

Share out the shells so that each merperson has
the same number of pink, white, and purple shells.

Each merperson
should have:

pink shells

white shells

purple shells

How Many More?

Count how many there are of each type of flower,
then write the calculations in the blank spaces below.

flower
A

flower
B

flower
C

flower
D

A [ ] – B [ ] = [ ]

C [ ] – D [ ] = [ ]

44

Cake Counting

Count the fruits on the cakes. Compare the numbers, and then write down how many fewer there are on the cakes on the right.

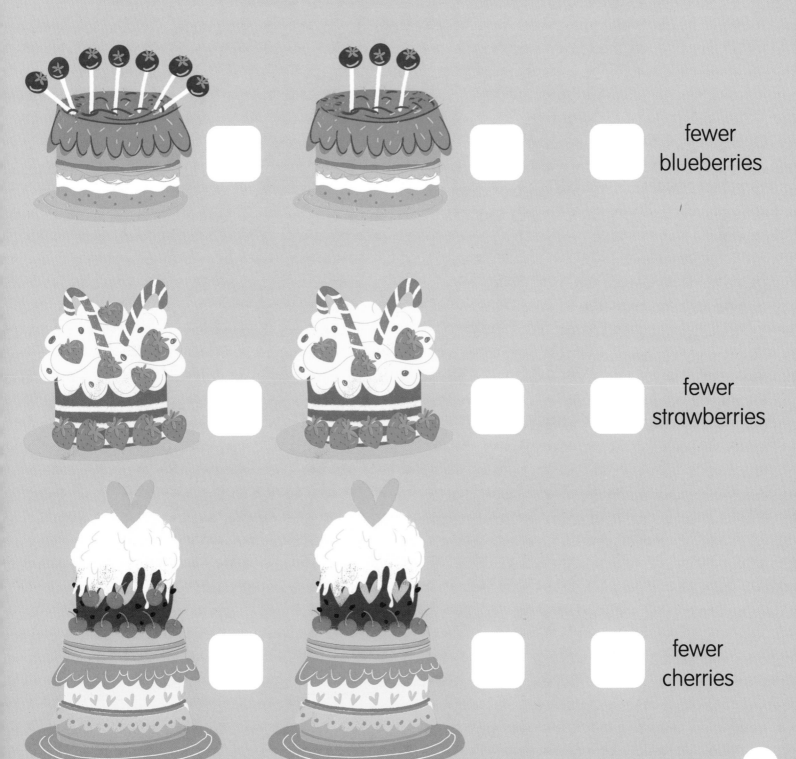

fewer
blueberries

fewer
strawberries

fewer
cherries

Count and Compare

Look at the two pictures and then answer the questions below.

How many shells decorate the harp in picture 1?

How many shells decorate the harp in picture 2?

What is the difference between the number of shells in the two pictures?

How many starfish decorate the harp in picture 1?

How many starfish decorate the harp in picture 2?

What is the total number of starfish in both pictures?

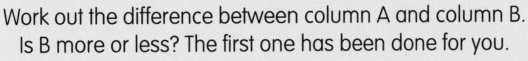

What's the Difference?

Work out the difference between column A and column B.
Is B more or less? The first one has been done for you.

A	B	Difference	
7	3	4	more / (less)
12	15		more / less
9	6		more / less
5	3		more / less
6	8		more / less
3	8		more / less
4	1		more / less
11	7		more / less

Counting in Tens

Myrtle is counting her treasure. Each chest has ten items in.
How many items are there altogether? Fill the empty boxes as you count.

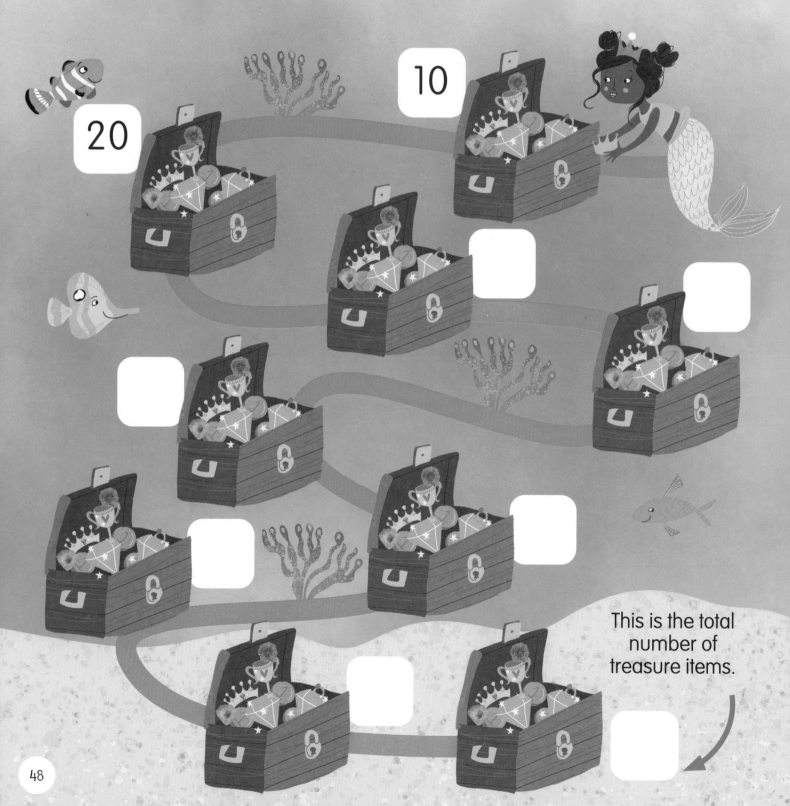

This is the total number of treasure items.

Leaping Dolphins!

Dolphin loves to leap. He can get to 20 in just 2 leaps.
Use the number line to answer the questions.

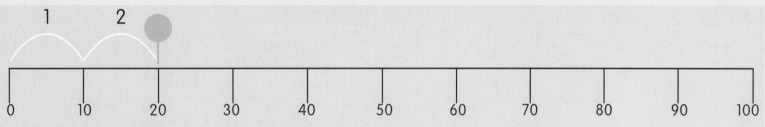

What number does he get to in three leaps?

What number does he get to in four leaps?

What number does he get to in five leaps?

What number does he get to in six leaps?

What number does he get to in eight leaps?

What number does he get to in ten leaps?

Start from 0 to count my leaps!

49

A Tale of Tails

Start at the bottom of each flowing tail and count in tens all the way up.

110

80

80

50

50

90

60

50

20

10

Cookie Counters

Sugarbelle is baking cookies for everyone.
She is arranging them in rows of ten.
Write down how many are in each batch below.

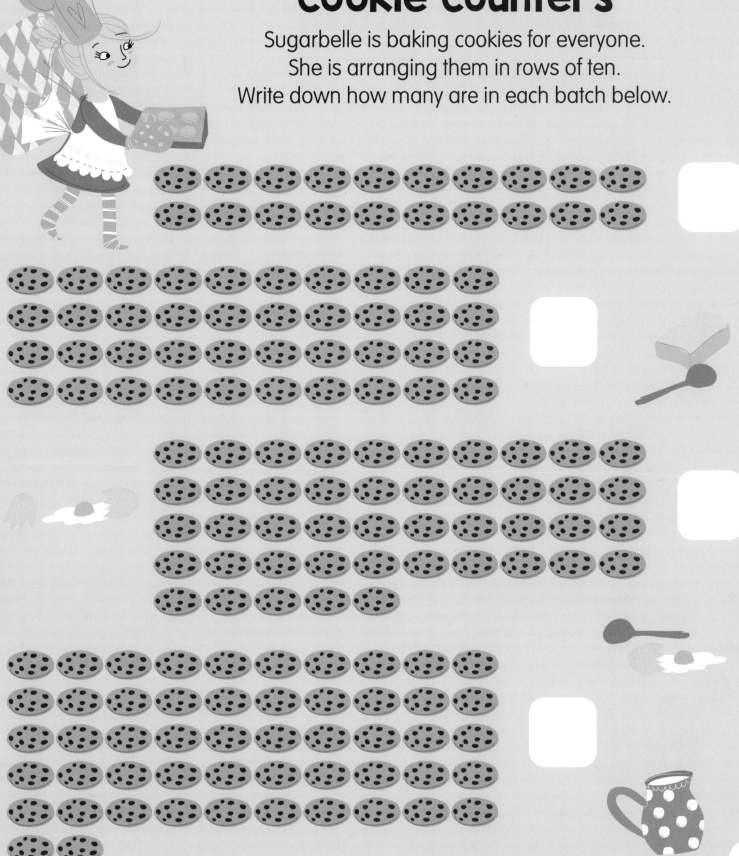

Snowball Fight!

Join in the fun by adding ten each time and writing the numbers on the snowballs.

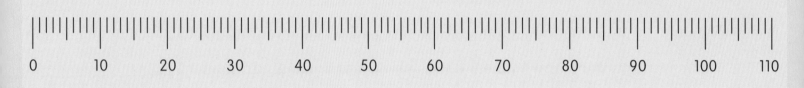

| 0 | 10 | 20 | 30 | 40 | 50 | 60 | 70 | 80 | 90 | 100 | 110 |

+10   +10   +10   +10

12   **22**

+10

21   **31**

+10

66

52

Saving Up

Ruby saves 10 coins every week.
How much money is in her purse each time?

$6 + 10 =$

$2 + 10 =$

$8 + 10 =$

$9 + 10 =$

$5 + 10 =$

$4 + 10 =$

Sweet Dreams

What is Shelley dreaming about?
Join the dots from 1 to 20 to find out.

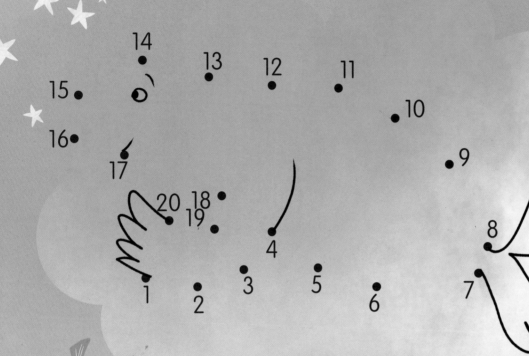

14
13   12   11
15   10
16   9
17
20 18
    19   8
4
1   3   5   7
2   6

Two by Two

Count up in twos to fill the blanks and help
Flossie fly to her friend Cupcake.

2   4   6

Party Time!

Match up the balloons so that each pair makes 20.

Twenty Twenty

Number bonds can make 20.
Can you think of pairs that add up correctly?

[ ] + 5 = 20

13 + [ ] = 20

9 + [ ] = 20

[ ] + 18 = 20

[ ] + 4 = 20

Don't forget, it doesn't matter which way round the numbers go when you add.

Twenty Pencils

Rainbow loves her pencils! She arranges them neatly in groups of 20. But her friends keep borrowing them. How many are left each time?

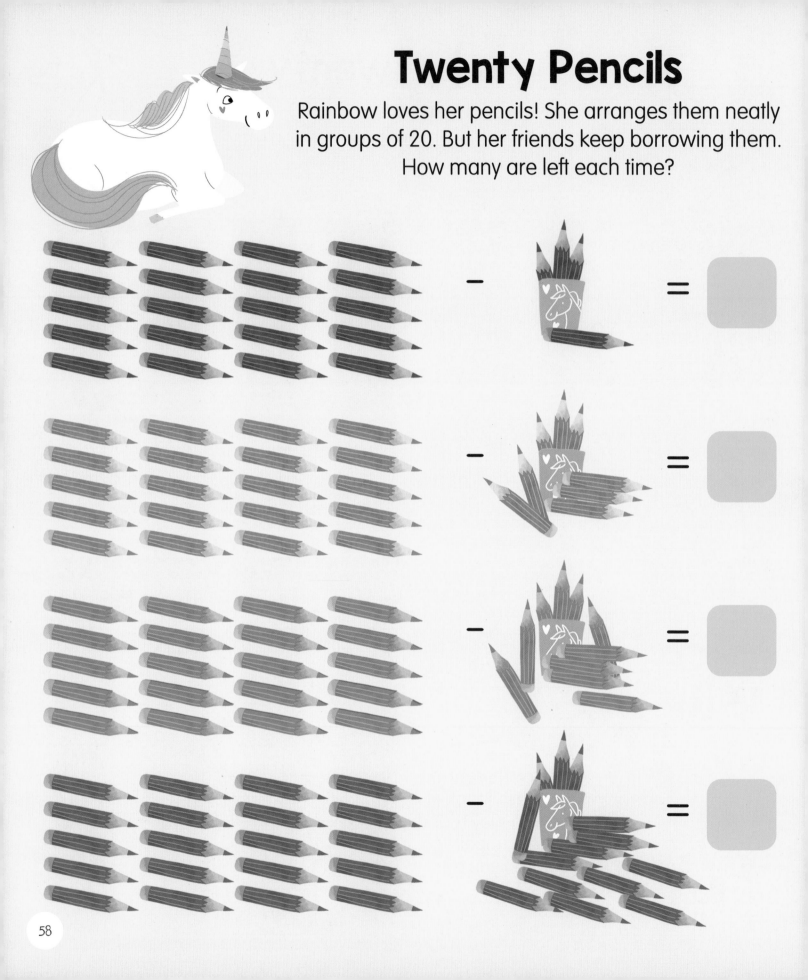

Witch's Brew

Help Midnight and his fairy friend Marietta to find the missing numbers that make 20.

$15 + \text{🎃} = 20$

$\text{🏮} + 2 = 20$

$10 + \text{🎃} = 20$

$\text{🏮} + 7 = 20$

$15 + \text{🎃} = 20$

$20 - \text{🏮} = 19$

$20 - 6 = \text{🎃}$

$20 - \text{🏮} = 11$

$20 - 16 = \text{🎃}$

$20 - \text{🎃} = 3$

Fairy Pairs

The fairies are testing each other on how quickly they can add pairs of numbers. How fast are you?

11 + 6 =

14 + 5 =

12 + 3 =

11 + 4 =

22 + 1 =

25 + 0 =

13 + 1 =

16 + 4 =

10 + 9 =

12 + 5 =

17 + 2 =

11 + 8 =

Tiara Time!

Ooh, look at the lovely tiaras for sale! Each is worth a different amount.
How much would it cost to buy two at a time, like the ones below?

| 20 | 15 | 10 | 3 | 5 | 2 |

 20 + 3 = 23    + =

+ =

+ =

+ =

+ =

+ =

Bridging

Learn how to solve problems by bridging through 10.
Use part of the second number to round
up to 10, then add the remainder.

8 + 6 = 14

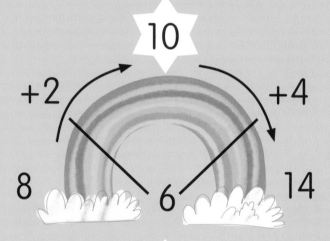

10

+2   +4

8   6   14

9 + 7 = [ ]

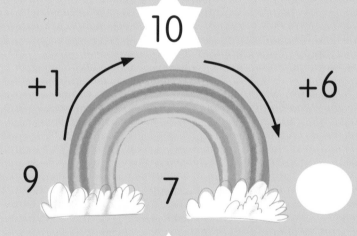

10

+1   +6

9   7

7 + 8 = [ ]

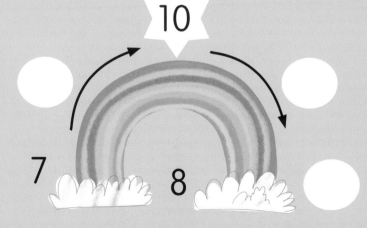

10

7   8

Bridging Back

Use bridging to help you with subtraction too.
Use part of the second number to round down
to 10 and then take away the remainder.

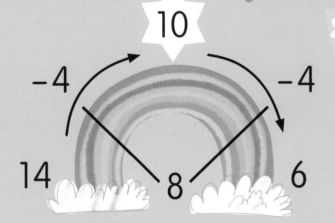
10
−4   −4
14   8   6

$14 - 8 =$  6

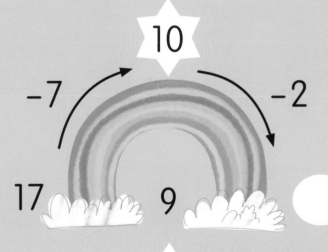
10
−7   −2
17   9

$17 - 9 =$

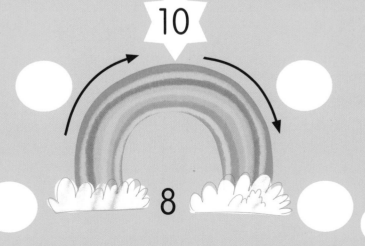
10
8

$16 - 8 =$

Merpeople's Problems

Find a shell with an answer match for each merperson's puzzle.

9 + 3

5 + 8

14

3 + 11

12

6 + 9

2 + 9

13

11

15

Add Them Up

Add the groups of numbers under each unicorn to find pairs with matching answers.

$6 + 5 + 3 + 4 =$

$2 + 3 + 8 + 8 =$

$10 + 5 + 2 + 4 =$

$5 + 4 + 7 + 2 =$

 and

 and

Thirsty Work

Petal has collected 100 strawberries. It takes 10 to make one pitcher of juice. Work out how many strawberries she will have left by crossing out the pitchers on the line below.

She makes two pitchers of juice. How many strawberries will she have left?

$$100 - 20 = \boxed{}$$

She makes another pitcher of juice. How many strawberries will she have left?

$$80 - 10 = \boxed{}$$

She makes four more pitchers of juice. How many strawberries will she have left?

$$70 - 40 = \boxed{}$$

Take It Slow

If Suzy snail can crawl 20 places in one day, how far can she get in two days? Starting from the right hand orange number on each number line, figure out how many places she can crawl in two days. The first one has been done for you.

Number line 1 (done): 42 → −20 → −20 → 82, marked from 0 to 100

Number line 2: start 36 → → 76, marked from 0 to 100

Number line 3: start 28 → → 68, marked from 0 to 100

Number line 4: start 13 → → 53, marked from 0 to 100

Build It Up

Write a number on the right hand tower that makes
100 when added to the number on the left.

45 +

22 +

68 +

79 +

Star Pupil

Find a pink star with the correct answer for each of the balloons.

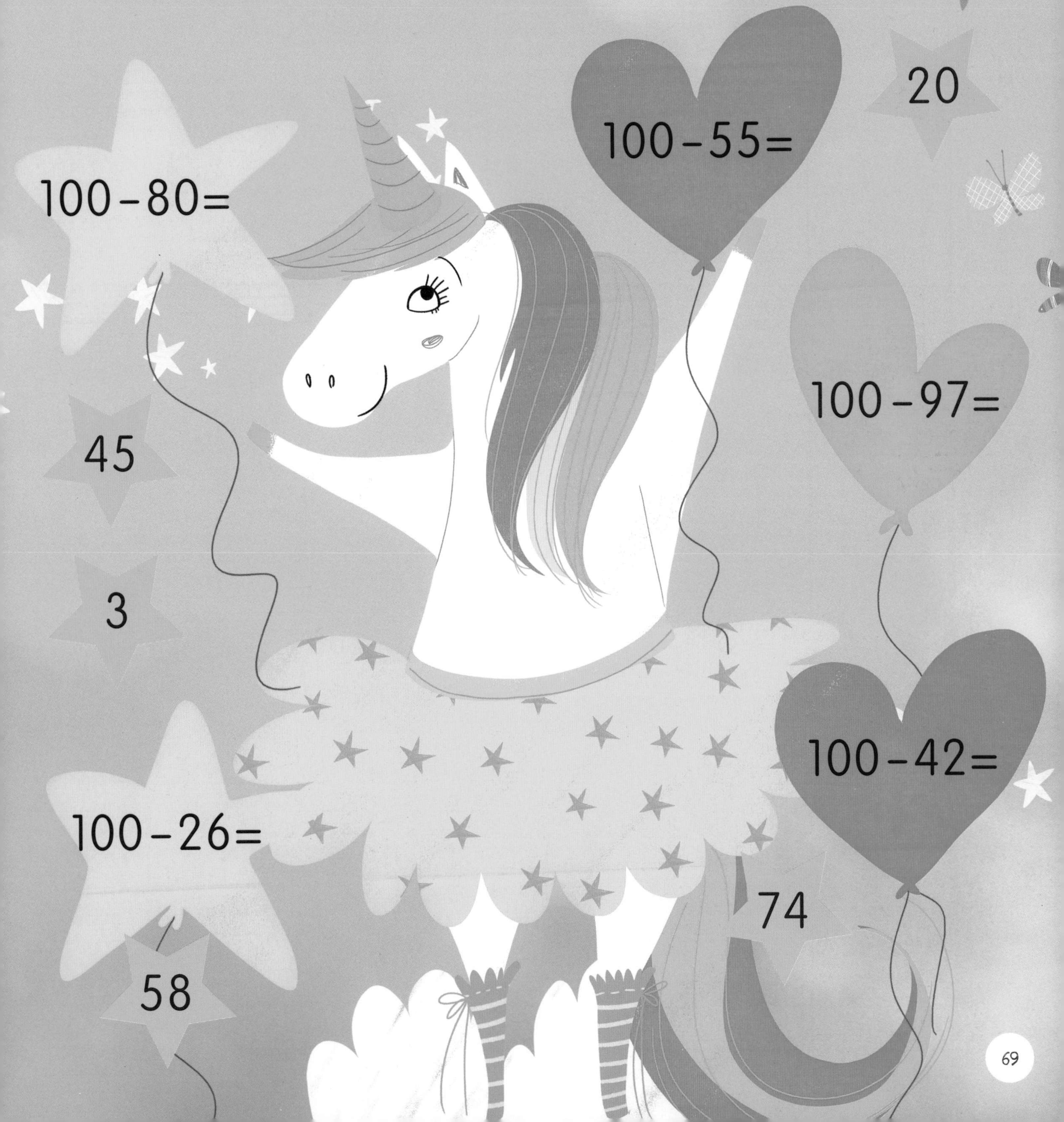

100−80=

100−55=

20

100−97=

45

3

100−26=

100−42=

74

58

Diamonds and Pearls

Which of the jewels is worth double the amount shown on each mirror?

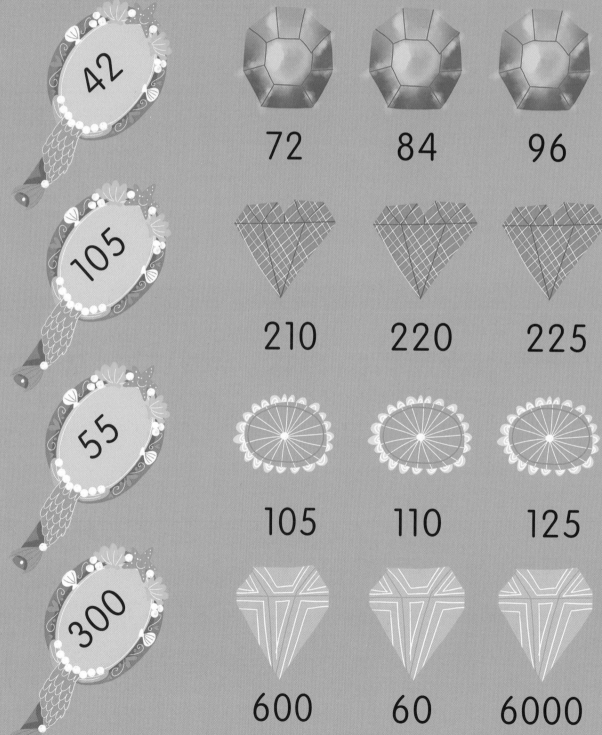

42

72   84   96

105

210   220   225

55

105   110   125

300

600   60   6000

Something's Cooking

Peaches has weighed out too much of her ingredients. Can you help her work out the correct ingredients, halving the number each time?

20

50

110

Under the Sea

Each of the creatures has three numbers. Can you write down the addition and subtraction facts, like the first example?

27   13

14

13	+	14	=	27
14	+	13	=	27
27	–	14	=	13
27	–	13	=	14

60   45

15

44   25

19

39   21

18

What's Wrong?

Now can you work out which fact is incorrect for each of the creatures?

18		7		
		11		

11	+	7	=	18
7	+	11	=	18
18	–	7	=	17
18	–	11	=	7

38		13		
		25		

13	+	25	=	38
25	+	13	=	38
38	–	13	=	25
38	–	25	=	25

52		29		
23				

23	+	52	=	52
29	+	23	=	52
52	–	23	=	29
52	–	29	=	23

47		11		
		36		

11	+	36	=	47
47	+	11	=	36
47	–	11	=	36
47	–	36	=	11

Fabulous Forty

Which of the answers
on the sandcastle
does not equal 40?

100 – 60

22 + 18

Double 20

35 + 5

90 – 40

Half of 80

29 + 11

52 – 12

More and Less

Fill in the columns to show numbers that are ten more and ten less than the numbers in the middle column.

ten more (add 10)		ten less (subtract 10)
	26	
	50	
	81	
	43	
	65	
	19	
	23	
	72	
	104	

Heading for Home

Help the fairies back to the castle. They must count upward on the stars, adding on 10 each time.

92

52

72

32

42

62

82

22

Owl Play

Find a matching partner for each owl that is holding a wand. Subtract 10 to help you pair them up.

Happy Birth-Yay!

The unicorns are buying flowers to celebrate Fliss's birthday. Work out which combination will cost the most.

 **25**    **10**    **8**    **20**    **15**

☐ **+** ☐ **=** ☐

☐ **+** ☐ **=** ☐

☐ **+** ☐ **=** ☐

☐ **+** ☐ **=** ☐

☐ **+** ☐ **=** ☐

☐ **+** ☐ **=** ☐

Birthday Treat

Each coin purse has a different amount of money. Work out which one is used to pay for each of the amazing birthday cakes.

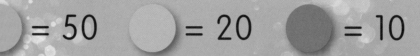 = 50   = 20   = 10

70

40

60

30

100

Festive Fun

Write down the calculation you need to do to find answers to each of the questions below.

Snowdrop hangs 12 green decorations on the tree. Ivy hangs 8 red decorations. How many more green ones are there?

Sparkle ties 4 red bows for Ivy, and 5 red bows for Snowdrop. How many has she tied altogether?

There are 7 presents under the tree. Trixie delivers 3 of them to friends. How many are left?

Holly bakes 12 Christmas cookies on Monday and 12 more on Tuesday. How many cookies has she baked altogether?

Hundreds, Tens, and Units

Help Prancer and Dancer put the numbers into the correct columns.

	Hundreds	Tens	Units
8			
80			
800			
10			
12			
122			
66			
660			
661			

Adding Three Numbers

If the three numbers always add up to 200,
which number is missing from each of
the items in Shelley's messy bedroom?

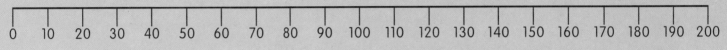

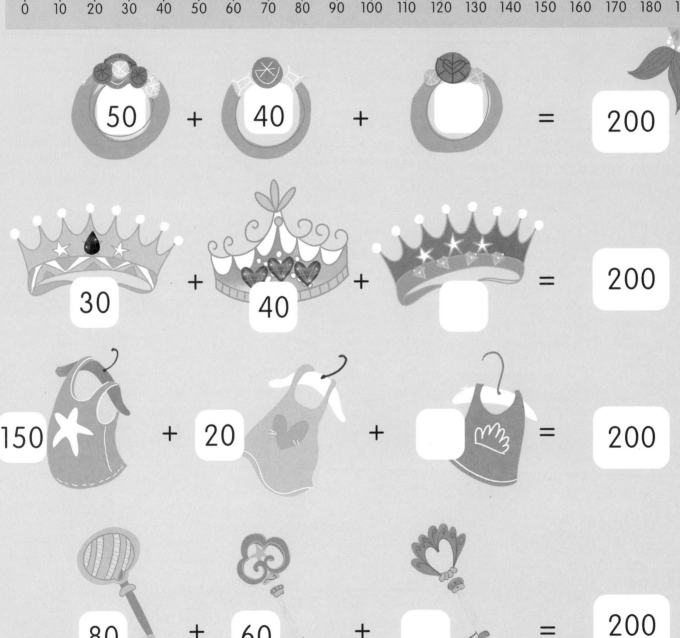

50 + 40 + ⬜ = 200

30 + 40 + ⬜ = 200

150 + 20 + ⬜ = 200

80 + 60 + ⬜ = 200

Work It Out

Can you work out the value of each toy? The numbers outside the grid are the totals from adding the rows and columns.

For Sale!

Each toadstool has a different value at the fairy market. Add up how much each selection costs.

7   12   10   25   6

Flossie's Feet

Flossie needs new shoes! If she has 50 coins to spend, work out how much change she would get if she bought any of these pairs.

38

26

50 − 38 = 12

30

18

13

45

High in the Sky

The unicorns love their kites! Use the numbers on each kite to answer the questions below.

What is double Charmer's number?

What's the difference between Charmer's number and Hollyberry's?

What is Starshine's number subtracted from Luna's?

What is half of Hollyberry's number?

What is Luna's number added to Hollyberry's?

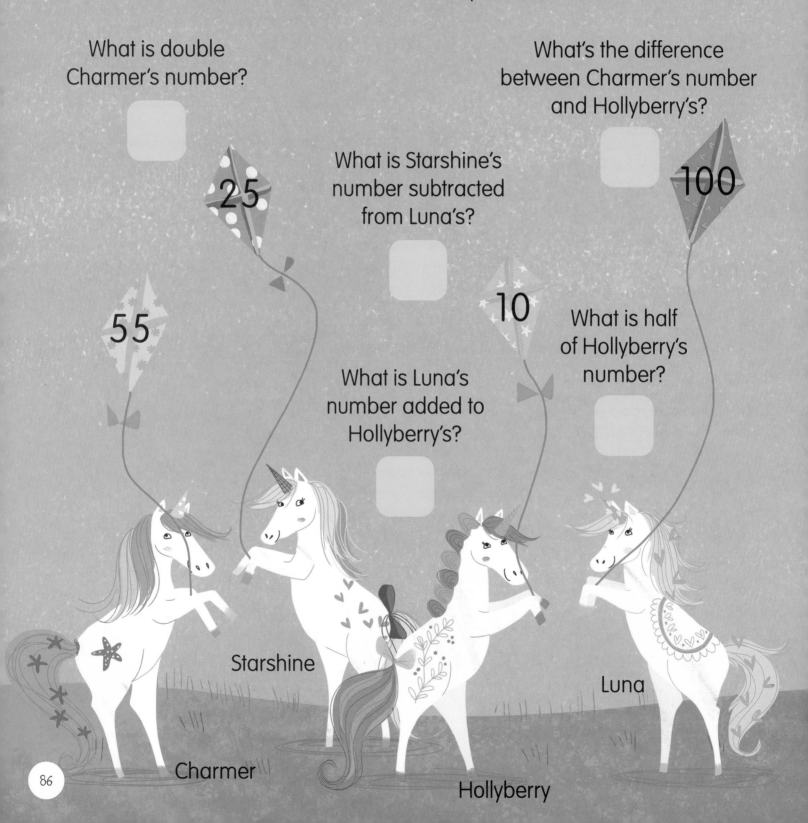

25

100

55

10

Starshine

Luna

Charmer

Hollyberry

Answers

5   Counting Fun

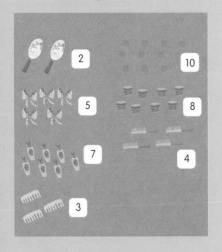

6   Dot to Dot

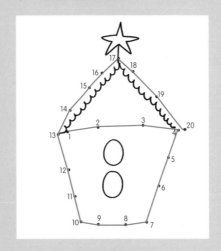

7   Under the Sea

8   Caterpillar Counting

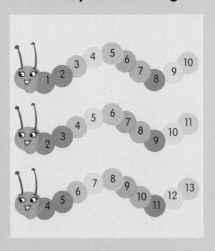

9   Hide and Seek

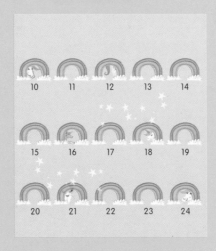

10   More, Please!

11 Less and More

one less (subtract 1)		one more (add 1)
4	5	6
7	8	9
3	4	5
5	6	7
1	2	3
6	7	8
9	10	11
8	9	10
2	3	4

12 Fairy Friends

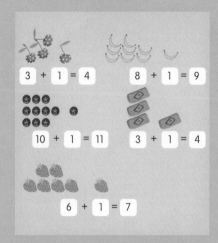

$$2 + 1 = 3$$
$$4 + 1 = 5$$
$$5 + 1 = 6$$
$$3 + 1 = 4$$

13 A Fairy Feast

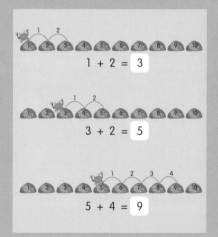

$$3 + 1 = 4 \qquad 8 + 1 = 9$$
$$10 + 1 = 11 \qquad 3 + 1 = 4$$
$$6 + 1 = 7$$

14 Mathemagical

$$2 - 1 = 1$$
$$3 - 1 = 2$$
$$5 - 1 = 4$$
$$4 - 1 = 3$$
$$6 - 1 = 5$$

15 Fly and be Free

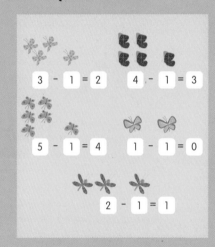

$$3 - 1 = 2 \qquad 4 - 1 = 3$$
$$5 - 1 = 4 \qquad 1 - 1 = 0$$
$$2 - 1 = 1$$

16 At the Beach

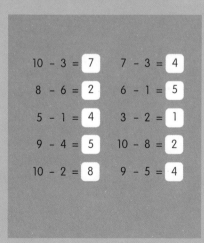

$$1 + 2 = 3$$
$$3 + 2 = 5$$
$$5 + 4 = 9$$

17 Clever Foals

$$2 + 5 = 7 \qquad 5 + 2 = 7$$
$$7 + 3 = 10 \qquad 6 + 1 = 7$$
$$4 + 2 = 6 \qquad 1 + 9 = 10$$
$$7 + 1 = 8 \qquad 6 + 3 = 9$$
$$3 + 2 = 5 \qquad 4 + 3 = 7$$

18 Giving Away Jewels

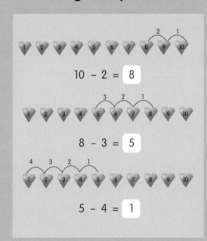

$$10 - 2 = 8$$
$$8 - 3 = 5$$
$$5 - 4 = 1$$

19 Lilac's Number Line

$$10 - 3 = 7 \qquad 7 - 3 = 4$$
$$8 - 6 = 2 \qquad 6 - 1 = 5$$
$$5 - 1 = 4 \qquad 3 - 2 = 1$$
$$9 - 4 = 5 \qquad 10 - 8 = 2$$
$$10 - 2 = 8 \qquad 9 - 5 = 4$$

20 A Hive of Activity

2 + **8**

5 + **5**

7 + **3**

1 + **9**

4 + **6**

21 Adding to Ten

10+0=10

0+10=10

1+9=10

2+8=10

3+7=10

4+6=10

5+5=10

6+4=10

7+3=10

8+2=10

9+1=10

22 Blown Away

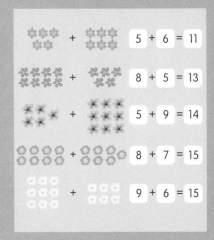

1 blows away? **9**

2 blow away? **8**

3 blow away? **7**

4 blow away? **6**

5 blow away? **5**

6 blow away? **4**

7 blow away? **3**

8 blow away? **2**

9 blow away? **1**

10 blow away? **0**

23 Remember, Remember

10−0=10

10−1=9

10−2=8

10−3=7

10−4=6

10−5=5

10−6=4

10−7=3

10−8=2

10−9=1

10−10 = 0

24 From the Trees

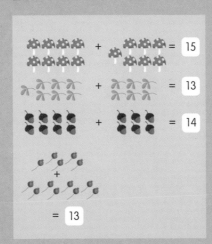

+ = **15**

+ = **13**

+ = **14**

+ = **13**

25 Say It With Flowers

+ 5 + 6 = **11**

+ 8 + 5 = **13**

+ 5 + 9 = **14**

+ 8 + 7 = **15**

+ 9 + 6 = **15**

26 From Zero to Hero

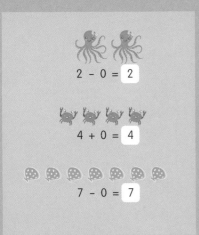

2 − 0 = **2**

4 + 0 = **4**

7 − 0 = **7**

27 Adding On

3 + 1 = **4**   1 + 3 = **4**

4 + 2 = **6**   2 + 4 = **6**

6 + 1 = **7**   1 + 6 = **7**

2 + 3 = **5**   3 + 2 = **5**

5 + 5 = **10**   2 + 2 = **4**

4 + 0 = **4**   0 + 4 = **4**

28 Paint a Rainbow

29 In the Pink

4 + 5 = 9   3 + 0 = 3

2 + 8 = 10   5 + 5 = 10

5 + 3 = 8   2 + 2 = 4

5 + 2 = 7   2 + 6 = 8

3 + 6 = 9   4 + 2 = 6

6 + 1 = 7

30 Sharing is Caring

⚞ − = 3

🍰 − = 3

🐚 − = 2

⚞ − = 1

🍓 − = 4

31 Happy Hair Day

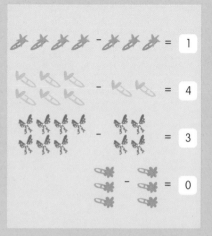

− = 1

− = 4

− = 3

− = 0

32 Take It Away!

10 − 5 = 5   9 − 2 = 7

6 − 2 = 4   10 − 6 = 4

7 − 5 = 2   12 − 6 = 6

8 − 6 = 2   8 − 1 = 7

10 − 0 = 10   3 − 1 = 2

4 − 0 = 4   9 − 2 = 7

33 Under the Sea

34 Caterpillar Calculations

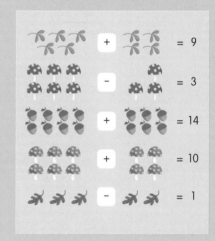

+ = 9

− = 3

+ = 14

+ = 10

− = 1

35 Rainy Days

12 − 2 = 10   6 + 4 = 10

5 + 5 = 10   3 + 7 = 10

36 Doubling Dots

3 + 3 = 6   5 + 5 = 10

2 + 2 = 4

6 + 6 = 12   4 + 4 = 8

37 Fishy Fun

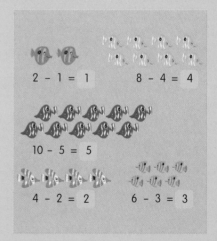

2 − 1 = 1   8 − 4 = 4

10 − 5 = 5

4 − 2 = 2   6 − 3 = 3

38 More Wishes

4 + 4 = 8

6 + 6 = 12

2 + 2 = 4

5 + 5 = 10

3 + 3 = 6

39 Pick Me!

4   6

7   5

40 A Perfect Match

8 − 3   11

5 − 2

6

8 + 3

9 − 3

10 − 3   3   5

41 Twin Twos

10 + 0 = 10   11 − 6 = 5

6 − 1 = 5   5 + 2 = 7

7 + 3 = 10   8 − 6 = ②

6 + 1 = 7   4 + 2 = 6

2 + 3 = 5   7 − 4 = 3

6 − 0 = 6   12 − 10 = ②

42 Money Match

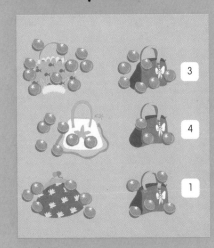

3

4

1

43 Shell Sharing

Each merperson should have:

pink shells   2

white shells   2

purple shells   3

44 How Many More?

flower A

flower B

flower C

flower D

A 6 − B 5 = 1

C 6 − D 3 = 3

45 Cake Counting

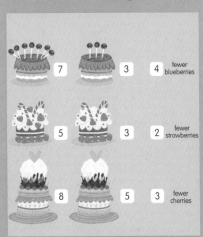

7   3   4 fewer blueberries

5   3   2 fewer strawberries

8   5   3 fewer cherries

46 Count and Compare

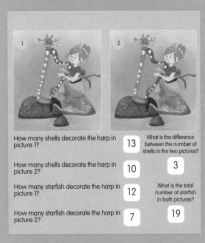

1   2

How many shells decorate the harp in picture 1?   13   What is the difference between the number of shells in the two pictures?   3

How many shells decorate the harp in picture 2?   10

How many starfish decorate the harp in picture 1?   12   What is the total number of starfish in both pictures?   19

How many starfish decorate the harp in picture 2?   7

91

47 What's the Difference?

A	B	Difference	
7	3	4	more / (less)
12	15	3	(more) / less
9	6	3	more / (less)
5	3	2	more / (less)
6	8	2	(more) / less
3	8	5	(more) / less
4	1	3	more / (less)
11	7	4	more / (less)

48 Counting in Tens

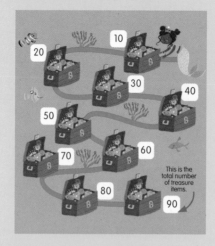

10
20
30
40
50
70
60
80
90

This is the total number of treasure items.

49 Leaping Dolphins!

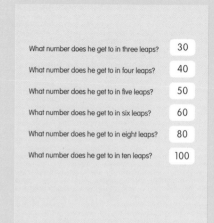

What number does he get to in three leaps?	30
What number does he get to in four leaps?	40
What number does he get to in five leaps?	50
What number does he get to in six leaps?	60
What number does he get to in eight leaps?	80
What number does he get to in ten leaps?	100

50 A Tale of Tails

120 110 100 90 80 50 40 30 20 10
100 90 80 70 60 50
90 80 70 60

51 Cookie Counters

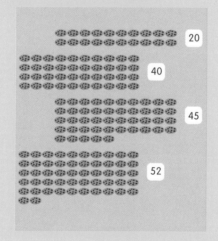

20
40
45
52

52 Snowball Fight!

+10   +10   +10   +10
12   22   32   42   52

+10
21   31   41   51   61

+10
66   76   86   96   106

53 Saving Up

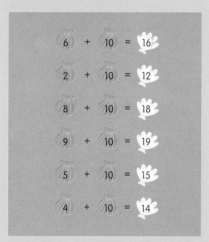

6 + 10 = 16
2 + 10 = 12
8 + 10 = 18
9 + 10 = 19
5 + 10 = 15
4 + 10 = 14

54 Sweet Dreams

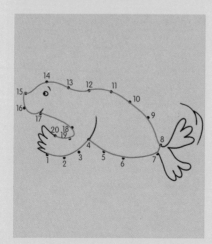

55 Two by Two

2 4 6 8 10 12 14 16 18 20 22 24 26 28 30 32 34 36 38 40

92

56 Party Time!

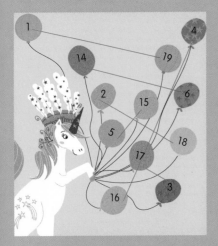

57 Twenty Twenty

15	+	5	=	20
13	+	7	=	20
9	+	11	=	20
2	+	18	=	20
16	+	4	=	20

58 Twenty Pencils

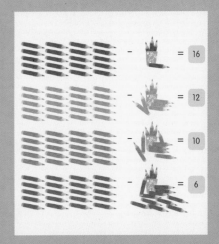

59 Witch's Brew

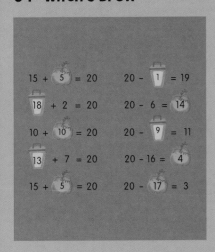

15 + 5 = 20   20 - 1 = 19
18 + 2 = 20   20 - 6 = 14
10 + 10 = 20   20 - 9 = 11
13 + 7 = 20   20 - 16 = 4
15 + 5 = 20   20 - 17 = 3

60 Fairy Pairs

11 + 6 = 17   13 + 1 = 14
14 + 5 = 19   16 + 4 = 20
12 + 3 = 15   10 + 9 = 19
11 + 4 = 15   12 + 5 = 17
22 + 1 = 23   17 + 2 = 19
25 + 0 = 25   11 + 8 = 19

61 Tiara Time!

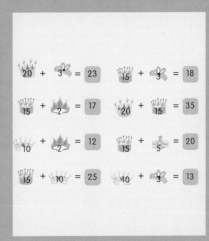

20 + 3 = 23   15 + 3 = 18
15 + 2 = 17   20 + 15 = 35
10 + 2 = 12   15 + 5 = 20
15 + 10 = 25   10 + 3 = 13

62 Bridging

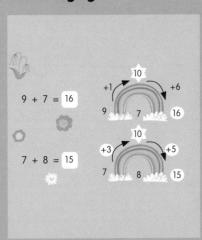

9 + 7 = 16
+1 [10] +6
9   7   16

7 + 8 = 15
+3 [10] +5
7   8   15

63 Bridging Back

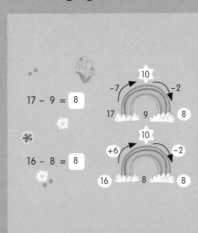

17 - 9 = 8
-7 [10] -2
17   9   8

16 - 8 = 8
+6 [10] -2
16   8   8

64 Merpeople's Problems

9 + 3 → 12
5 + 8 → 14 (13)
3 + 11 → 14
6 + 9 → 15
2 + 9 → 11

93

65 Add Them Up

$6 + 5 + 3 + 4 = $ 18

$2 + 3 + 8 + 8 = $ 21

$10 + 5 + 2 + 4 = $ 21

$5 + 4 + 7 + 2 = $ 18

A and D
B and C

66 Thirsty Work

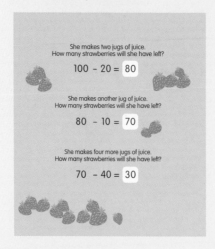

She makes two jugs of juice.
How many strawberries will she have left?

$100 - 20 = $ 80

She makes another jug of juice.
How many strawberries will she have left?

$80 - 10 = $ 70

She makes four more jugs of juice.
How many strawberries will she have left?

$70 - 40 = $ 30

67 Take It Slow

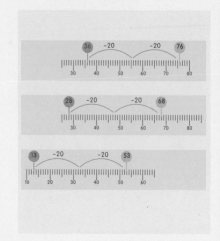

68 Build it Up

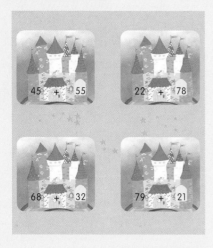

$45 + 55$

$22 + 78$

$68 + 32$

$79 + 21$

69 Star Pupil

$100 - 80 =$ $100 - 55 =$ 20

45

$100 - 97 =$

3

$100 - 26 =$ $100 - 42 =$

58   74

70 Diamonds and Pearls

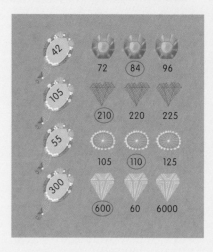

42

72   (84)   96

105

(210)   220   225

55

105   (110)   125

300

(600)   60   6000

71 Something's Cooking

10

20

25

50

55

110

72 Under the Sea

27   13   14

13	+	14	=	27
14	+	13	=	27
27	-	14	=	13
27	-	13	=	14

60   45   15

15	+	45	=	60
45	+	15	=	60
60	-	15	=	45
60	-	45	=	15

44   19   25

19	+	25	=	44
25	+	19	=	44
44	-	19	=	25
44	-	25	=	19

39   18   21

18	+	21	=	39
21	+	18	=	39
39	-	18	=	21
39	-	21	=	18

73 What's Wrong?

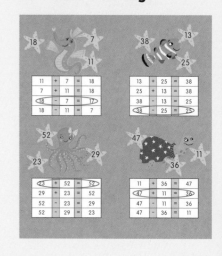

18   7   11

11	+	7	=	18
7	+	11	=	18
18	-	7	=	17
18	-	11	=	7

38   13   25

13	+	25	=	38
25	+	13	=	38
38	-	13	=	25
38	-	25	=	25

52   23   29

23	+	52	=	52
29	+	23	=	52
52	-	23	=	29
52	-	29	=	23

47   11   36

11	+	36	=	47
47	+	11	=	36
47	-	11	=	36
47	-	36	=	11

74 Fabulous Forty

100 – 60
22 + 18
Double 20
35 + 5
90 – 40
Half of 80
29 + 11
52 – 12

75 More and Less

ten more (add 10)		ten less (subtract 10)
36	26	16
60	50	40
91	81	71
53	43	33
75	65	55
29	19	9
33	23	13
82	72	62
114	104	94

76 Heading for Home

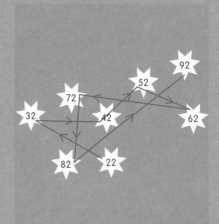

92
52
72
32
42
62
82
22

77 Owl Play

102
84
96
95
74
86
69
105
92
79

78 Happy Birth-Yay!

$25 + 15 = 40$
$8 + 10 = 18$
$20 + 8 = 28$
$25 + 10 = 35$
$25 + 8 = 33$
$10 + 15 = 25$

79 Birthday Treat

70
40
60
100
30

80 Festive Fun

$12 - 8 = 4$

$4 + 5 = 9$

$7 - 3 = 4$

$12 + 12 = 24$

81 Hundreds, Tens, and Units

	Hundreds	Tens	Units
8	0	0	8
80	0	8	0
800	8	0	0
10	0	1	0
12	0	1	2
122	1	2	2
66	0	6	6
660	6	6	0
661	6	6	1

82 Adding Three Numbers

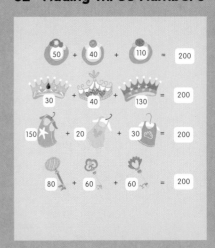

$50 + 40 + 110 = 200$
$30 + 40 + 130 = 200$
$150 + 20 + 30 = 200$
$80 + 60 + 60 = 200$

95

83 Work it Out

5   3

2   10

84 For Sale!

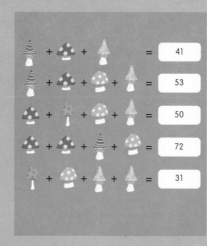

= 41
= 53
= 50
= 72
= 31

85 Flossie's Feet

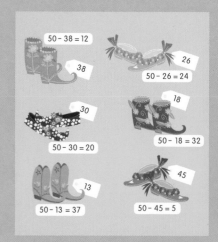

50 - 38 = 12
38
26
50 - 26 = 24
18
30
50 - 18 = 32
50 - 30 = 20
13
45
50 - 13 = 37
50 - 45 = 5

86 High in the Sky

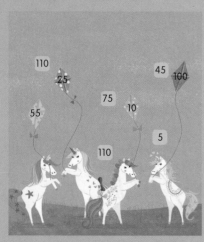

110
25
45 100
55   75   10
5
110